D1614375

Building Britain's Locomotives

The erection of a Great Western *King*
class locomotive at Swindon works
in 1927.

BUILDING BRITAIN'S LOCOMOTIVES

James W. Lowe

Moorland Publishing

© **J.W. Lowe**   1979

ISBN 0 903485 78 8

Photoset by Advertiser
Printers Ltd, Newton Abbot
and printed in Great Britain by
Redwood Burn Ltd,
Trowbridge & Esher for
Moorland Publishing Co Ltd,
PO Box 2, 9-11 Station Street,
Ashbourne, Derbyshire,
DE6 1DZ.

Contents

Acknowledgements

The author and publisher would like to thank the following for the use of photographs:
A.C.Baker/T.D.A.Civil Collection: 1, 19, 23, 25, 26, 39, 54, 55, 58, 61, 66, 131-5, 150; Andrew Barclay Sons & Co: 53, 136-8; British Rail (Eastern Region): 125; British Rail (London Midland Region): 47, 116, 118, 127, 142; British Rail (Western Region): 15, 16, 18, 21, 22, 24, 27, 28, 32-6, 38, 40, 46, 57, 62-5, 71, 73-98, 110-114, 141, 146, 147; British Steel Corporation, Sheffield Division: 2-13, 30; British Steel Corporation, Tubes Division, Corby: 41-5; R.H.Clark: 56, 128; J.Crawley Collection: 17, 29, 37, 48, 72, 121, 143; L&GRP (courtesy David & Charles): 115; the late W.L.Good: 140; Hunslet (Holdings) Ltd: 14, 60, 67, 69,
129; Imperial Chemical Industries: 120; Kearns-Richards Division, Staveley Machine Tools Ltd: 59; Manifold Collection per Dr J.R.Hollick: 20; Merseyside County Museum, Liverpool: 149; Mitchell Library, Glasgow: 130, 148; Photomatic (Wholesale) Ltd: 117, 119, 122-4, 126, 139; City of Salford (Libraries): 51, 52, 144; Carl Zeiss, Oberkorchen, W. Germany: 99.

Thanks are also due to the following who have willingly extended their help and for providing some of the photographs: Messrs A.C.Baker; R.C.Bond; R.H.Clark; G.Horsman; G.Milligan (University of Glasgow); C.Blick and R.Purdie (British Steel Corporation).

Introduction

In steam days the main interest of the general visitor to a locomotive works was the erecting shop and probably the same is true today. On conducted tours where the route taken was specially planned and strictly adhered to, the main workshops, because of the time available, were the only ones on view. As each party might consist of schoolboys, business men, clergymen and a general cross section of the community each with their own particular interests, some of them could be satisfied and others not. At Swindon in the 1920s and 1930s mid-week organised visits were very popular and tours were made of the carriage and locomotive departments. On the other hand the railway societies favoured visits on Sundays, their prime aim being to see all the locomotives in and around the works and in the running sheds as there would be far more there than on a week day. In my experience at Wolverhampton and Swindon, the majority of these week-end visitors were not really interested in how the parts required to build a locomotive came into being, or the procedures adopted for their overhaul, and any attempt to point out some manufacturing technique would usually be met with a blank stare.

The erecting shop was the focal point of operations where all the parts and assemblies converged and to the visitor this was the highlight of the tour. There were two main types of erecting shops: one consisted of a shop or bay with two pit roads, one on each side, and a service road between the two pits on which the heavy material such as boilers, cylinders and wheels were brought. Two overhead cranes able to travel from one end of the shop to the other at high level were capable of lifting the completed locomotive on to the centre road for subsequent removal. In some shops of this type the building was high enough for the cranes to lift one locomotive over another. In larger factories this arrangement of two long pits and centre road would be multiplied by the addition of similar bays, the number being governed by the requirements for building new locomotives and overhauls. The other type of erecting shop consisted of a traverser serving a number of pits side by side, on one or both sides of the traverser. This type occupied a much larger area with the width of the traverser taking up non-productive space, but had the advantage of more working area.

Originally each locomotive being built was the responsibility of one erection gang, and probably up to five gangs would be building five locomotives at the same time. Later other methods were tried and some adopted. Certain gangs specialised in one phase of locomotive erection; cylinders and motion, wheels and axleboxes, etc. Either each gang moved from locomotive to locomotive to do their operations, or the gangs were static and the locomotive brought to them. These methods usually applied to railway workshops where reasonable quantities of say, ten, twenty, or more locomotives of the same type were built, without other types intervening. Some of the larger contracting builders introduced similar methods.

Another arrangement used the roundhouse, two examples being the early works at Gorton and Derby. Where relatively small narrow-gauge locomotives were built they were jacked up for access between frames and no pits were used. Even so pits were often provided for 2ft gauge systems for oiling and maintenance, but they did not give the shed staff much working room.

In this collection of photographs the object has been to show some, but by no means all, of the operations and machinery necessary to manufacture steam locomotives of both the tank and tender types. The section on wheels shows mainly the production of disc wheels for tenders, wagons and carriages. Locomotive wheels have gone through a variety of phases. The earlier ones had built up spokes rivetted to a wheel rim, later cast-iron wheel centres were introduced and finally they were manufactured from steel castings which were usually bought out and machined in the railway workshops. The tyres were shrunk on and a retaining ring fitted or kept in place by bolts through the wheel rim into the tyre.

The section on boilers gives some examples of round top and Belpaire fireboxes, the boiler assembly finally comprising smokebox, boiler and firebox. It will be seen that a firebox, particularly the Belpaire type is a very complicated and expensive assembly involving many operations.

Fitting shop equipment varied a great deal as the main work was the assembly of parts of the motion, regulator assembly, safety valves, injectors, ejectors, screw reversing gear and a host of other parts. A bench and vice were the main requirements for each fitter, with arbor presses, grinding wheels, faceplates and other ancillary equipment. As machining techniques improved so the hand fitting operations decreased and the majority of the work was carried out in the erecting shops which usually had benches, vices and other equipment next to the pits.

Many machine tools were built specially for one operation or for a number of operations on one part. The majority of machine tools used were lathes — centre, automatic, turret and capstan — as well as milling, grinding and drilling machines. Some standard machines were adapted or converted for special operations and full use was made of jigs and fixtures. Foundry work used techniques and equipment as in any other steel, iron and non-ferrous foundries.

Locomotive works of any size were equipped with a laboratory for chemical analysis and also a fully equipped test house where tensile, impact and shear tests were carried on samples of materials supplied. Lifting gear, chains and ropes were also tested to comply with statutory requirements.

Many departments and processes could not be included in this book, but this representative selection illustrates most of the stages involved in building steam locomotives. The original intention was to acquire period photographs, but surprisingly few really old illustrations were obtainable. Nevertheless the photographs that are included here show many fine erecting shop scenes. The details depicted will be of great use to model engineers and will interest all those who love the steam locomotive, bringing back memories and a whiff of smoke and oil.

The Drawing Office

The private builder of locomotives, according to his size and facilities, supplied locomotives to customers' requirements and specifications, to their drawings, or from their standard range. In the larger railway workshops the design and manufacture of locomotives was the responsibility of the Chief Mechanical Engineer or Locomotive Superintendent and the Chief Draughtsman for each design. After these designs were finalised the drawing office staff would make working drawings of each part to enable them to be manufactured in the various shops. So those responsible for the design and details of each class of locomotive were essentially trained engineers. It has to be borne in mind that these detailed parts had to be designed and drawn taking into consideration the machine tools and plant available to carry out their manufacture with the shape and accuracy required.

Close liaison had to be maintained between the various shops and the drawing office. Standardisation of parts helped to keep down the costs, but this sometimes inhibited a break away from an accepted method of design or manufacture and thus could sometimes prevent or retard improvements in design.

The actual draughtsmanship was of a high standard and up to the 1920s the general arrangement drawings were often painted in contrasting colours and indeed were almost works of art. Present day methods are more functional with original drawings being traced or inked over and micro-filmed to facilitate storage. After having had experience in the various workshops apprentices' training included a spell in the drawing office.

1

1   The beginning of it all — the drawing office of W.G. Bagnall Ltd, Stafford, in 1930. Work was done on simple drawing boards supported by benches, in contrast to the modern equipment used in most offices today. The staff included designers, buyer, chief draughtsman, draughtsmen, female tracers and typists. This drawing office was completely rebuilt and enlarged in 1952-3. Note the framed photographs of the firm's products.

Wheels and Tyres

Early wheels were made in four pieces: the hub or nave, the spokes, the rim and the tyre. Running on the early plate rails, the wheels had no need for flanges, but with the introduction of edge rails a flange had to be added to the rim or tyre. To enable the tyre to be self-centering on the track a coned profile tyre was introduced as early as 1821 and later a standard profile was adopted.

Early designs were varied, with wheels similar to road carriages made from wood with iron rims, others were of cast iron in one piece including the nave, spokes and rim. The slender cast-iron spokes frequently fractured and as malleable-iron spokes were found to be far superior these were bolted or rivetted to the cast-iron rim and a malleable-iron tyre was shrunk on the rim by heating the tyre, which after fitting gripped the rim by contracting as it cooled. A more satisfactory way of using cast iron was by casting the centre, heavy H-section spokes, and the rim with a tyre of steel. Steel tyres were first used by the LNWR at Crewe in 1859. This type of wheel was generally used on locomotives for shunting and medium speed work.

The next step was the introduction of cast-steel wheel centres with the hub, spokes and rim as one casting, and this became the most common type used. An added safeguard for the retention of the tyre on the rim was the Gibson Ring hammered into a recess machined in the bore of the tyre. This was invented by Mr J Gibson in the 1860s when he was Carriage and Wagon Superintendent at Swindon and it was a simple but effective device.

The final manufacturing operation on locomotive coupled wheels is balancing to ensure smooth running. The weight of the revolving parts such as crank pin, big end and part of the connecting and coupling rod are calculated and balance weights bolted to each wheel. Then the reciprocating parts such as small end, crosshead, piston and piston rod, part of the motion and rods are totalled in weight. By experience it was found necessary to balance about two thirds of this weight, and so additional weights were added. The wheels are placed in a balancing machine and are revolved at a speed usually equivalent to a track speed of 60mph. Each journal is smeared with red lead and pointed rods are brought into contact with them as the axle revolves on spring loaded centres. Out-of-balance locations are thus indicated and corrections made. Molten lead is then poured between the spokes and retaining plates on each side of the spokes equivalent in weight to the balance weights put on the wheels for the operation.

Most of these illustrations of the manufacture of wheels show the solid type of wheel and wheel centre used for wagons, carriages and tenders.

2   The tyre mill at the Steel, Peech and Tozer works, United Steel Companies Ltd, Rotherham, about 1950. A tyre blank is being punched under a 2,000-ton forging press with a manually operated table. The blank has been heated in a furnace to 1,000–1,250°C, according to the type of steel so that it is in a plastic form and easily worked and formed. The remaining illustrations in this section are from this works unless otherwise stated.

3 A close up of the roughing stand where the pre-heated tyre is shaped by rotating form rollers under hydraulic pressure. The effect of hot working of the material increases the steel's tensile strength and decreases its ductility.

4 Rough rolling the tyre, which is supported on radial rollers, by a roller on the side face and another on the tyre profile.

5 The tyre is now on a horizontal finishing mill with a sizing device for width.

6 A group of workmen in 1898 outside the tyre mill of Steel, Peech & Tozer, Rotherham. Out of twenty-six men only six, more youthful types, do not sport moustaches!

6

7 The wheels on which the tyres are fitted are forged on a 6,000-ton hydraulic press. One wheel is being forged, while a completed wheel is being removed. The two operators are cooling the dies with water hoses.

8 The forged wheel has then to be rolled to size and here a solid wheel is in the finishing stand of a wheel mill. The wheel has to be reheated between the various operations.

9 United Steel Companies Ltd, Owen & Dyson Works, in 1947. Finish boring two railway wheels to fine limits on a Duplex Vertical Boring Mill before pressing them on to the axles. The outside profile of the wheel has been finished machined.

10 Forging an axle on a 7-ton steam hammer at United Steel Companies Ltd, Steel, Peech & Tozer (Ickles works) in 1953. The end of the axle is gripped and turned mechanically and the whole operation is controlled by the operator on the left. Forging gives the axle more strength than if it was made from solid drawn bar.

11 Rough machining an axle in a lathe with a multi-tool set up at the United Steel Companies Ltd, Sheffield Division, in 1947.

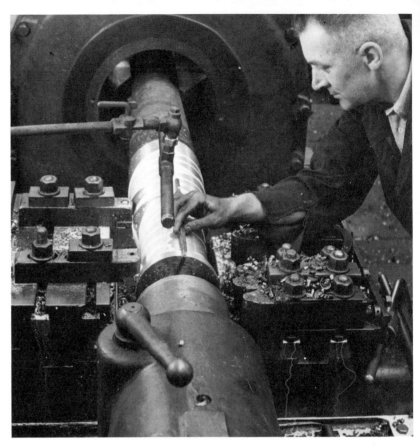

12 Rolled steel railway wheels awaiting dispatch for finish machining at United Steel Companies Ltd, Steel, Peech and Tozer Works, about 1950.

12

13 Hydraulically pressing finished wheels onto an axle at United Steel Companies Ltd, Owen & Dyson Works, about 1950. The wheels are pressed on to the axle which has shoulders to locate the wheels and is machined to give the correct gauge distance between the wheels.

14 Boring locomotive wheels for crank pins, at the Hunslet Engine Co, Leeds, 1932. In front of the machine is a pair of driving wheels with inside cranks, also wheel centres and tyres. The operation was known as quartering and great care had to be taken to ensure that the crank pins were exactly 90⁰ to one another and the correct distance from the wheel centre.

15 The wheel shop at the Great Western Railway's Swindon works in 1947. Fitting a key into a keyway in an axle and wheel. Note the built-up inside cranks which are set at 90° to each other.

16 An assortment of wheels in the Barry Shops of the GWR (ex Barry Railway) in 1926. A wheel lathe is on the left and on the right are various machines including radial-arm drillers in the foreground.

16

17 The 6ft 8in diameter driving wheels for a Class A4 streamlined Pacific at the LNER's (formerly Great Northern Railway) Doncaster Works in 1935. This pair of wheels was driven by all three cylinders. Note the inside crank, balance weights and the crank pins with square milled ends to take the eccentric crank. Doncaster Works built 2,224 steam locomotives from 1867 to 1957.

18 The wheel shop at the Cardiff West Yard works of the GWR (ex Taff Vale Railway) in 1926. Note the monorail crane and narrow gauge track for bogies to carry materials.

19 The works of W.G. Bagnall Ltd, at Stafford, about 1930, showing equipment for wheels, a connecting rod on a slab milling machine and a wheel press. A pair of driving wheels with its eccentrics and big-ends already fitted is being lifted by the overhead crane.

20 The Stoke works of the North Staffordshire Railway showing a wheel ready for tyre fixing. The marking-off table on the left has a coupling rod being marked for centres and other important dimensions.

Forge, Smithy and Foundry

Forging is one of the oldest methods of metal working, heating the material to red heat and hammering it into the shape desired. This could be to finished dimensions or rough forged to be subsequently machined. For larger components the steam hammer was introduced by James Nasmyth in 1839 enabling large shafts to be shaped, and with dies fixed to the base and hammer head intricate parts could be produced. For hand forging the smith used a hearth on which a coke fire was brought up to heat by bellows or mechanical draught. The tools used were a great variety of hammers, tongs, setts and swages, many of which the smith made himself and used on the heated material on an anvil. A quenching tank was placed nearby. The advantage of making a forging as compared with machining from bar stock is that the flow of metal caused by forging gives a far stronger part as well as economy in material. Drop hammers worked by friction were also used and continuous-motion forging machines were introduced for the production of nuts, bolts and other parts used in quantity.

Founding or casting is as old as forging and was used by the ancient Greeks and Romans. Iron and non-ferrous castings are made by first producing a wooden pattern of the article required, due allowance being made on the dimensions for contraction of the casting on cooling. The pattern is pressed into special moulding sand housed in moulding boxes which are split in half to allow the pattern to be withdrawn. When ready for casting the top half of the moulding box is weighted down to prevent the molten metal escaping at the joint. A pouring hole and vent is formed in the mould. For hollow casting cores have to be made and baked, and carefully fixed in the mould. Pattern making and moulding are both extremely skilled and complicated work. Many parts which are used in locomotive manufacture are castings such as cylinders, brass and gunmetal fittings which have to be machined and other operations performed on them before they are ready for fitting to the locomotive.

Some parts such as brake blocks, railway chairs and other parts used in quantity, were produced in the larger railway works in mechanised foundries as a continuous process with special power-operated moulding machines with jolting machines to compact the sand, which is fed into the boxes from chutes. The metal is melted in cupolas: pig and scrap iron, coke and limestone are added in layers and when molten the metal is tapped into ladles which are used for pouring the molten metal into the moulds. After cooling the moulds are opened and the sand knocked away to expose the castings. The same method in principle is employed for non-ferrous castings. Test pieces and samples are tested to establish the strength and composition of the metal.

21 A typical smiths' shop at the Machen works of the GWR (ex Brecon and Merthyr Railway) with a great variety of work piled up in the foreground, in 1926.

22

23

22 This view of the smithy at the Cathays works, Cardiff of the GWR (ex Taff Vale Railway) in 1926 contrasts sharply with the tidiness of the Machen smithy. This is a type of shop which is difficult to keep tidy, but in this case it is worse than usual. A great aid for the smithy was the steam hammer and one can be seen in the right background with a smaller one in the left foreground. Most of the work done here was for carriages and wagons.

23 A posed picture in the smithy at W.G. Bagnall's works, Stafford, in 1931. Hearths and anvils are arranged along the walls with steam hammers at the rear and centre.

24 The brass foundry at the GWR's Oswestry works (ex Cambrian Railways) showing moulding boxes and a variety of hand tools.

25 W.G. Bagnall's pattern shop about 1929, showing a multitude of wooden patterns including cylinders, driving wheel and chimney. Foreman George White stands near the stove, and along the wall are a variety of woodworking machines.

26 W.G. Bagnall's iron foundry in 1925. The moulders in the foreground are preparing moulds in the sand floor, while behind them sand boxes for smaller castings are being prepared.

27 Swindon 'J' shop in 1951 showing the complicated half moulds necessary for producing the cast cylinders for the BR class 4 4-6-0s.

28 The casting of the class 4 cylinders in 1951 at Swindon 'J' shop. Note the large weights on the boxes to keep the two halves of the mould together during the casting operation.

29 A general view of the iron foundry at the Doncaster works of British Railways (Eastern Region) in 1954, showing the variety of work including cylinder moulds being constructed and various cores.

30 Early locomotives had no springs, then steam springs were used to a limited extent which were in effect pistons attached to each axle housed in cylinders fixed to the underside of the boiler. Steam springs were rather a misnomer as the cylinders were on the water side. Difficulty was experienced by leakage past the pistons. Leaf springs were in common use at an early stage and were used to the end of steam locomotion. Volute and spiral springs were also introduced and were used where leaf springs would take up too much room, particularly over the trailing wheels which were usually under the cab. Springs have two functions, to provide a good suspension over each journal so as to take the shock loads off the engine itself, and secondly to provide a means of adjusting the weight on each axle by slackening or tightening the spring hangers. Equalising beams connecting springs on each side were used on some locomotives but were eventually discarded in favour of independent springs. Leaf or laminated springs are composed of flat steel plates varying in number and dimensions according to the loading. The top plate is the longest and has forged ends forked and drilled to take the spring hanger pin at each end. Each subsequent plate is shorter to give the spring characteristic and are fixed together with a central forged buckle. A pin drilled through the buckle and plates and rivetted over prevents the plates moving endways. The springs are given a camber of some 3in to 4in without load which is reduced when under load to about half this figure. Springs are made from carbon steel, oil hardened and tempered. Here at the United Steel Companies Ltd, Steel, Peech and Tozer works in 1952 the leaves of the springs are rivetted together and set in a hydraulic machine, after which they are tempered.

Boilers

Early boilers were of cast iron or wrought iron rivetted construction with a single flue tube or more usually a return tube which gave a more efficient heat transfer. Pressures at this time did not exceed 50 lb/in^2. Since then multi-tubular boilers became universal and a host of additional fittings were introduced which mainly were for feed-water heating, early superheating, combustion chambers and different types of fireboxes. Hammered wrought-iron plates rivetted together were replaced by steel plates in the 1860s which allowed the boiler pressure to be increased and more recently nickel steel was used for higher pressure with no increase in weight.

The design of the steam producer was perhaps the most important part of locomotive design. Even if the remainder of the engine was well established in the layout of the front end, valve gear, cylinder clearances, blast pipe, etc, if the boiler did not produce the steam as and when required, the locomotive would not meet traffic requirements. To correct the deficiencies resulted in additional cost and loss of service revenue and this happened many times.

Boiler shop equipment was never complicated and mainly involved various types of rolling machines for shaping the boiler plates and inner and outer fireboxes, hydraulic presses with adjacent furnaces for pressing the firebox and boiler end plates.

The two main types of firebox were the round top and Belpaire. The latter was invented by Alfred Belpaire, a Belgian, in 1864 but it was not until 1891 that this design was introduced by a British railway on one of its own locomotives. This was a 0-6-2T Manchester, Sheffield and Lincolnshire Railway No 7, built at Gorton. The advantages of the Belpaire firebox were the flat top which could be directly stayed to the inner firebox which followed the same contours, greater cross-sectional area at the firebox tube plate where the heat was greatest, and increased volume of steam space improved even more by the conical boiler barrel which was extensively used. Although more expensive to produce this type of firebox was more accessible for maintenance.

One other type of firebox which should be mentioned was the Wootten type, a wide firebox whose base passed across the frames, being too wide to rest between them. The almost square firebox was shorter than an equivalent firebox between the frames, which facilitated firing and good heat distribution.

Most inner fireboxes were made from copper, that metal being a better conductor of heat. Steel was also used, resulting in a lighter firebox, but the heat transfer was not as great.

Steam produced in a simple boiler is in direct contact with the boiling water and is known as saturated or wet steam. If this steam is collected and passed through nests of tubes housed in larger tubes above the smoke tubes it becomes dryer and its volume increases, for a constant steam pressure. Wilhelm Schmidt was the first to apply high temperature superheating at the end of the last century, as distinct from various steam dryers tried out by other designers. Variations of Schmidt's design were introduced by Robinson, Gresley,

Churchward, Aspinall, Maunsell and others. Full advantage was obtained from superheated steam by using its expansive properties and this led to fuel and water economy.

With the higher temperatures of superheated steam, carbonisation of valves and cylinder surfaces was much greater and required more suitable lubricants fed by mechanical force feed, sight feed displacement, and hydrostatic lubricators to alleviate the problem.

31 Diagrams showing the differences between the main types of boilers and fireboxes and their basic construction.

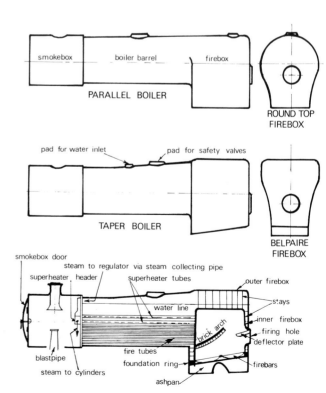

32 Pressing the throat plate for a BR class 4 4-6-0 boiler at Swindon works in 1951. The throat plate is the connection between the rear end of the boiler barrel and the outer firebox. The metal blanks, seen on the left, were heated in the furnace in the background before being shaped in this hydraulic press. Four men are holding the hot blank in position and the shaped bottom die is clearly seen. This machine was installed in 1899 and had a total pressing power of 650 tons.

33 The pressed steel throat plate partly drilled, at British Railways Swindon works in 1951.

34 GWR Swindon works, 1927. The inner copper firebox assembled with temporary bolts ready for rivetting.

35 GWR Swindon works, 1927. The foundation ring has been fitted onto the copper inner firebox, and this is now ready for fixing into the outer firebox casing. The holes drilled for the stays and tubes are clearly seen.

36 GWR Swindon works, 1927. The firebox assembly showing stays, tube plate and the pattern of rivetting. The firebox is upside down to facilitate rivetting over the stays in the lower half.

37 A Wootten type inner firebox with a grate area of 41.25 ft^2 for a class A4 Pacific at Doncaster works in 1935. The foundation ring and tube plate have been fitted, the stay holes have been drilled and the unit is ready for fitting into the outer firebox.

38

38 A hydraulic gap rivetter, rivetting the longitudinal seams of a boiler shell at GWR Swindon works in 1927. The joints are covered by straps and rivetted together. Compare the size of the boiler with the man at floor level.

39 The boiler shop at Bagnall's works, Stafford, in 1930. A boiler with a round-topped firebox is in the rivetting pit on the right suspended by an overhead crane. Beyond the pit on its side is a boiler for a GWR 0-6-OPT.

40 A rig for machine-tapping stay holes at the GWR Swindon works in 1947. The machines were counterbalanced and driven by compressed air. Note the shape of the rear end of a typical Belpaire firebox.

39

41 Inserting the small tubes in a boiler for a Garratt locomotive at Beyer, Peacock and Co Ltd, Gorton, Manchester in 1957. The steel tubes are Stewarts and Lloyds electric resistance welded type, and the larger tubes when fixed will house the superheater elements. The boiler and firebox dimensions clearly show the advantages of the Garratt design which enabled large boilers to be fitted. This boiler was part of an order for forty-six 4-8-2 + 2-8-4 locomotives for Rhodesia Railways (Nos 715-760). The Beyer, Peacock works numbers were 7780-7825.

42 The front view of the same boiler showing the small tubes being fitted.

43 Boilers for 0-6-0ST 'Austerity' shunting engines at the Hunslet Engine Company, Leeds, in 1956. The Austerity engines were of Hunslet's design and hundreds were built by them and other locomotive manufacturers during World War II for the War Department. This batch was for the National Coal Board. Here the steel tubes are being expanded with a compressed-air driven machine.

44 Inside the firebox of an 'Austerity' boiler at Hunslet Engine Works in 1956, beading over the tubes with a hydraulically-operated percussion tool.

45 A view inside a boiler in the process of being tubed, looking towards the firebox, showing the firebox stays and the main steam pipe. This boiler was for an Indian State Railways class WG locomotive being built at the North British Locomotive Company's Hyde Park Works, Glasgow (formerly Neilson Reid and Co), in 1955.

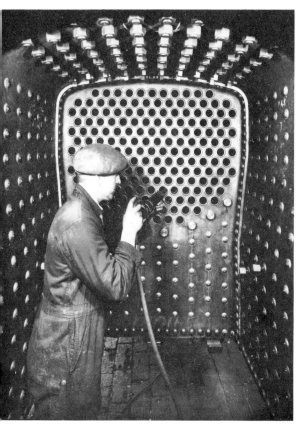

46 A comparison of smokebox
front plates at the GWR Swindon
works in 1910. On the left is a built-
up rivetted type while on the right is
one pressed out of one piece. The
latter was a cheaper and more
satisfactory method after the tool
and die cost had been taken into
consideration.

47 The boiler shop at British
Railways' Crewe Old Works in 1963
showing new boilers and others
being repaired. The boiler at the
lower left has had its foundation ring
removed exposing the stays which
can be seen. Behind is an ex LNWR
round-topped boiler.

48 The boiler for No 3401 *Bantam
Cock* class V4 (a smaller version of
the V2 2-6-2) on temporary bogies
at the LNER's Doncaster works in
1940. This picture shows the
Wootten firebox, the parallel front
section and the tapered rear section
of the boiler barrel. The tapered
section was joined by a horizontal
seam with rivetted plates. The V4
was the last design by the then Chief
Mechanical Engineer, Sir Nigel
Gresley.

49 GWR Swindon works 'A' shop in 1933, showing a boiler being lagged with asbestos plastic composition applied wet. Drying was assisted by heating up water in the boiler by means of a steam pipe connected to the back of the firebox.

50 GWR Swindon works 'A' shop in 1933 with a similar boiler ready to drop into its frames. The safety-valve pipework and cover have been fixed as well as the cleading and chimney.

51 Nasmyth Wilson and Co Ltd, Patricroft, Lancashire, with a boiler complete with all the fittings on the back of the firebox, the chimney and dome in position and the ash pan on an adjacent pit.

52 Nasmyth Wilson and Co Ltd, Patricroft, Lancashire. The tank shop showing tanks, bunker and cab completed.

53 Sheet metal work on tanks and cabs at Andrew Barclay Sons and Co Ltd, Kilmarnock. On the right is a saddle tank on its side and a typical Barclay cab half built with port-hole type windows.

Fitting and Machining

One could say that early locomotives were practically hand made as the majority of the work was done by smiths, wheelwrights and millwrights. Over the years hand operations were gradually reduced, but not entirely eliminated. The main parts of the early steam locomotives were similar to those of the stationary engines and pumps built almost a century before the Pen-y-daren locomotive, and boilers for generating low-pressure steam go back to ancient times. Early locomotives show clearly the transference of a boiler, cylinders, valve gear and flywheel to a wagon-type frame and wheels.

Fitting as distinct from erecting was a highly skilled trade even if the tools used such as a file, scraper, hammer and chisel were the basic necessities. The development of machine tools over the years was an important contribution to the accuracy and precision to be found in the manufacture of steam locomotives over the last thirty to forty years of building. Apart from standard machine tools many were adapted for various operations on components, being sometimes kept set up for one particular operation but flexible enough to adjust to different sizes. Special grinding machines were built for journals and crankshafts, lathes and balancing machines for wheels, profile milling machines, borers and many others. Most of the machine tools seen in these pictures were driven from overhead shafting by a forest of flat belts; these did not disappear until individual electric motor drive became common.

54 The machine shop of W.G. Bagnall Ltd, Stafford, about 1930. Marking-off tables are at the front right and boring machines on the left. A narrow-gauge service track runs along the centre of the workshop.

54

55 Machining the face of a connecting rod on a vertical milling machine for an Assam Railways and Trading Company locomotive at W.G. Bagnall Ltd, about 1930. Note the flame-cut hole in the connecting rod on the floor.

56 The Midland and Great Northern Joint Railway's Melton Constable works in 1913. Here is a veritable forest of belts and shafting in the machine shop. A wheel lathe is on the left, and smaller lathes in the foreground.

57 Swindon 'AM' shop in 1927. A special purpose drilling machine is drilling a *King* class smokebox saddle which is cast integrally with the inside cylinders.

58 W.G. Bagnall Ltd, Stafford, in 1931 with an axlebox being slotted ready for bearing metal on the left. The planing machine on the right is machining big-ends straps.

59 The Gorton works of the Great Central Railway in 1899, with a Kearns horizontal borer with inside cylinders for a class 11A 4-4-0 designed by H. Pollitt. The cylinders were 18½in x 26in and the piston valves were positioned beneath the cylinders. Note the cored steam ports at the end of the cylinders. The casting has been bored and faced, drilled, tapped, and the studs screwed in. On the top face the exhaust has been faced and studded ready for the blast pipe and the two angular steam inlets have been similarly dealt with.

60 Drilling locomotive frames with two radial drilling machines at the Hunslet Engine Co, Leeds, in 1929. Four frames are being drilled simultaneously.

61 On the right drilling frames for a GWR 87XX 0-6-OPT at W.G. Bagnall Ltd in 1931. In the foreground a frame is being profiled by flame cutting.

62 End milling the faces of a fabricated tender drag box at British Railways' Swindon works in 1951.

63 Machining the header for a three-row superheater at BR Swindon works in 1951.

64 Milling the face of a foundation ring for a *King* class boiler at the Swindon works in 1927. The foundation ring is made of forged steel and it is the 'spacer' at the base of the firebox between the inner and outer shells.

65 Drilling a foundation ring on a radial drilling machine at Swindon in 1927.

65

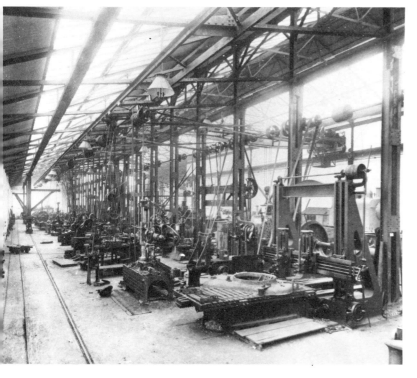

66 The fitting bay at W.G. Bagnall Ltd, Stafford, about 1930, with parts ready for assembly including connecting and coupling rods, axles, sand boxes, and slide valve stirrups. The erecting shop is on the right.

67 The machine shop at Avonside Engine Co Ltd, Bristol, in 1905, showing planing machines, etc. On the first machine is a firebox throat plate for a raised round top firebox. The next bay contains two engine units for Great Northern Railway railmotors. This photograph was probably taken shortly after the firm had moved to St Philips from the Avon Street Works.

68

69

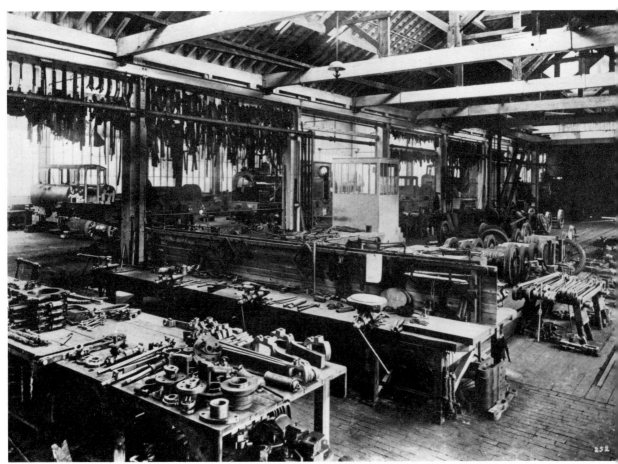

68 Part of the toolroom 'O' shop at the GWR Swindon works in 1934. Many tools such as taps, dies, milling cutters, drills and reamers were made here.

69 The Hunslet Engine Co, Leeds, in September 1899. Fitting benches showing motion parts including eccentrics and connecting rods. An interesting feature shown on the edge of the nearest bench is the eye ends of coupling rods with a short stub of rod before being fire welded to the centre portion of the rod. This was the usual practice with wrought-iron coupling rods. In the background is part of the erecting shop with City and South London Railway electric locomotives. They were an order from Crompton & Co Ltd for ten frames, wheels, cabs etc. The finished axles were sent to Cromptons to have the armatures wound on, then returned to Hunslet and the locomotives assembled except for all electrical fittings, motors and motor suspension springs. No Hunslet works numbers were allocated as the building was done under spares order No 21656. Two had already been built in 1898 (order 20638). The other locomotive in the bay is Manchester Ship Canal No 16 *Galveston* ready for dispatch (Works No 700).

Valve Gears

Numerous types of valve gear were used in the early days of locomotion including plug valves, tappets, loose eccentrics for reversing, while the two eccentric forked-gab motion did away with hand valve levers. The study of lap and lead, admission and exhaust events was an important step in using the expansive property of steam. A further advance was the invention in 1842 of the link motion, where a slotted link was connected to forward and reverse eccentrics. By this means 'linking up' could take place, so regulating the amount of steam admitted for each stroke.

Until the introduction of superheating the most common type of valve was the slide valve which passed over the cylinder ports, the movement of the valve being controlled by the valve motion. Much has been written about valve gears but suffice it to state that the two most common types used were the Stephenson's link motion and Walschaert's valve gear and these are shown in the diagram. The Stephenson valve gear's main characteristic is that the 'lead' increases as the motion is linked up, whereas in the Walschaert type the lead is constant, that is, the opening of the admission valve before the piston reached the end of its stroke was always the same. The 'linking up' or cut-off was effected by moving the reversing lever from full forward gear to various positions notched into the lever quadrant. Screw reversing could give more accurate settings. Other types of reversing mechanisms were steam or compressed-air operated.

Poppet and rotary valve gear have also been used but very little development took place. It will be appreciated that efficient steam distribution and exhaust was most important, coupled with the critical dimensions of the blast pipe and chimney.

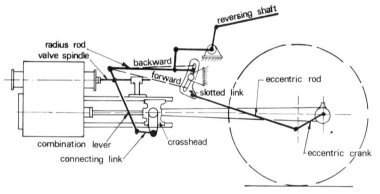

WALSCHAERT'S VALVE GEAR

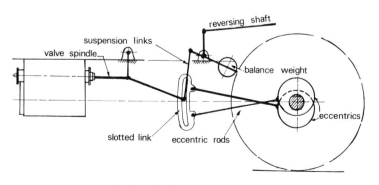

STEPHENSON'S VALVE GEAR

70 Diagram of the two most widely used types of valve gear.

71 Stephenson valve gear on the bench at the GWR Swindon works in 1915, showing the reversing shaft beneath, the eccentric rods and the slotted links. The reversing shaft lifts or lowers the slotted links by means of the suspension links connecting the reversing shaft arms to the top of the slotted links.

72 The front end of a class A1 Pacific locomotive with conjugate valve gear in the erecting shop of the Doncaster works in 1932. This shows the method of actuating the inside cylinder valves by means of extensions to the two outside valve rods. The longer lever gave a ratio of 2:1 with a fixed pivot and the shorter lever had two equal arms with a floating pivot: one end connected to the inside valve rod and the other to the left-hand outside valve rod.

73 The built-up crank axle for a *Castle* class locomotive at the GWR Swindon works in 1924. This axle comprised nine separate parts which were pressed together hydraulically and then keyed. Note the extended webs for balancing.

74 A woman worker filing off sharp edges on a coupling rod at the GWR works, Swindon, in 1947. Due to war time shortage of labour, women were found very adaptable on various types of work and many remained until male labour returned after the war, which took some time.

Locomotive Erection

The pioneer locomotive builders used the facilities of colliery workshops to produce the early 'mechanical horses' using shear-legs to lift the boiler on to the chassis. After the Rainhill Trials of 1829 various engineering firms decided to enter the field of locomotive building and workshops began to re-equip themselves with machinery to deal more efficiently with the bits and pieces peculiar to this particular industry.

All the parts were delivered to the erecting shops, some as units and some as assemblies. Most railways and locomotive contractors favoured the straight road type of shop with or without pits, but for gauges one metre wide or over, pits between the rails were found to be more satisfactory, particularly for locomotives with inside cylinders and valve gear. Others were of the round-house type with central turntable and radiating pits, such as the old erecting shops at Derby and Gorton, and where there was plenty of room, the traverser in the centre of the shop with pits on either side, were used.

For any of these arrangements, the essential requirement was perfectly level rails on substantial foundations. In some works due to heavy use this accuracy was not maintained and this was clearly apparent when the home railways ordered large numbers of locomotives from private contractors; they were inspected at various stages by the railways' inspectors who found in some cases that the initial frame levelling and alignment left a lot to be desired. Heavy ground plates were introduced on substantial and carefully levelled concrete foundations, upon which the jacks could be placed, sometimes in slots to support the frames for erection and for some of the specialised operations.

An interesting side light on erection was the record set up by the LNWR at Crewe in February 1888 when a standard 17in 0-6-0 'Coal' engine No 1140 was built in 25½ hours. Not to be outdone the Great Eastern Railway's works at Stratford put together a 0-6-0 (No 930) in 9 hours 57 minutes. Of course these times do not include the manufacture of the parts required, but are for assembly only. Nevertheless to assemble a locomotive in under ten hours required meticulous planning. A more realistic time set up by Neilson & Co, at their Hyde Park Glasgow Works, was an order for twelve locomotives for Japan received in September 1894. This entailed the designing and detailing of the locomotives in the drawing office, ordering and making all the parts, and assembly. The final erection was carried out with such speed that the first complete locomotive was turned out in November, taking sixty-five days from start to finish. Since then no doubt this time was cut down even more.

Overhead cranes were used, the majority of shops having two down each bay so that the locomotive could be lifted bodily for wheeling. Where it was too heavy to lift in one piece each end was dealt with separately, the other end resting on packing.

Early frames were made from wrought iron, but in 1886 the first steel frames were introduced enabling the longest frame to be in one piece. Bar frames were used by Edward Bury from 1830 to 1848 when plate frames of wrought iron were used. American practice used bar frames and the modern ones were of cast steel using complex patterns which included the cylinders, smokebox saddle, axlebox guides and stretchers as one huge casting.

The major improvements to facilitate erection, apart from the floor level plates, involved machinery such as drilling machines moving along parallel with the frames, grinding machines, and valve setting gear and this will be seen quite clearly in the following photographs.

Private building firms could concentrate on building new locomotives with just the occasional overhaul, as distinct from the railway workshops which had to keep all their locomotives in running order. This involved rebuilding, general overhauls and all repairs which could not be carried out in the running sheds, although the larger sheds were equipped with a lifting shop where quite heavy repairs could be effected, so relieving the main works. Not all the railway workshops built their own new locomotives, and many were supplied by private contractors, leaving the works to do all overhauls.

In the following photographs the complete sequence of erection from frames to painted locomotive is followed through for three different locomotives at different periods. All three locomotives are being built in the 'AE' shop at Swindon and show a 31XX class 2-6-2T 'Prairie Tank' being built in 1906, a 60XX *King* class 4-6-0 in 1927 and in British Railways days a class 4 4-6-0 in 1951. The later photographs show the improvements in alignment techniques, using optical methods and the special purpose grinding machines for grinding the horn faces between which the axle-boxes fit.

31XX class, 1906

75 The frames are laid out for one of Lot 159 (Nos 3131-49). All the brackets and horn blocks are marked out ready for drilling from the holes already drilled in the frames. Note the boiler-carrying plate in the foreground. No 3141 is partly completed on the left.

76 The frames are set up on jacks for No 3146 and the cylinders are in position. Each cylinder and half the smokebox saddle was a separate casting, the two halves faced and bolted up and positioned astride the frames. The method of lining up the cylinders and horn centres with whipcord and straight edges across the horn faces was used until the introduction of the Zeiss equipment, shown later in use by British Railways for class 4 locomotives.

77 The boiler is now in position resting on the saddle, support plate and firebox brackets. The chimney, buffers, buffer beams and footplating have been fixed. Behind is a vertical boiler for a Railmotor and to the left on the next pit is No 40 the four cylinder 4-4-2 in the process of being constructed with its inside cylinders and motion in position.

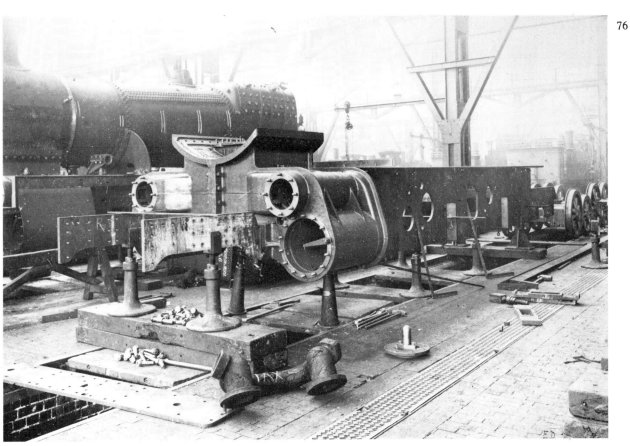

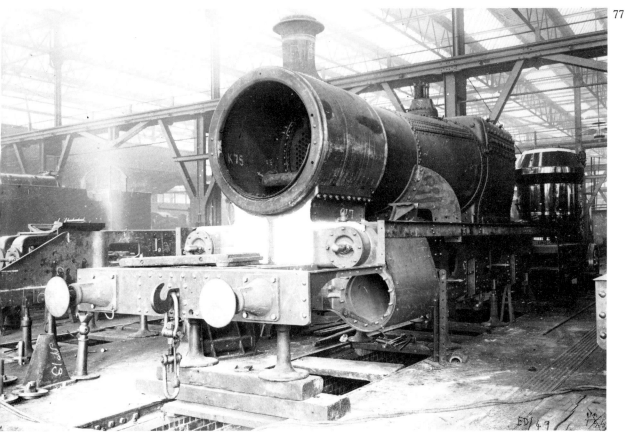

78 The boiler has been lagged and the cleading partly fixed; the tanks (complete with number plate: No 3140) have been fitted; the slide bars are ready for the crosshead (on the floor); and axleboxes will be tried up the horn blocks. The smokebox door has been hung and fitted.

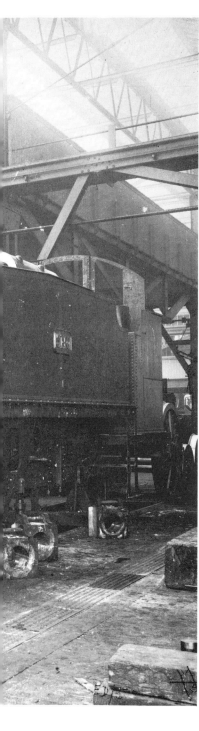

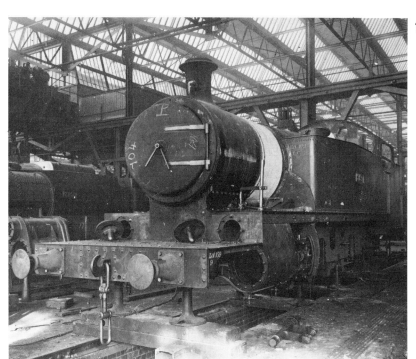

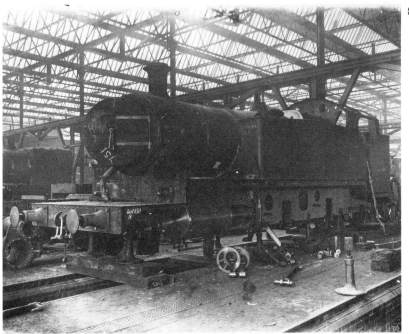

79 The crossheads have now been fitted and the cab and bunker completed. Note the reversing shaft on the floor, with its volute spring for ease of reversing. (No 3139)

80 The pistons have been fitted to the crossheads, the cylinder covers bolted in place and the polished cleading fixed. The eccentrics and motion is ready for assembly. Note the lengthy reversing lever leaning against the cab. (No 3138)

81

81 Here is No 3137 almost completed. The pony truck has yet to be fitted. The locomotive is being moved to the top of the shop on the electric traverser for valve-setting and painting.

82 A complete locomotive of this class painted grey for photographic purposes. No 3120 was built in a previous batch in 1905.

82

King class, 1927

83 Swindon 'AE' shop again, but now 21 years later, building a much larger engine, the celebrated and powerful Great Western *King* class four-cylinder express locomotive. The pairs of frames were sent from the frame shop already drilled. The various brackets are being marked out for drilling. The general arrangement drawing is being examined by the bowler-hatted shop foreman, Mr Dew and the leading fitter of No 3 gang. The rectangular holes in the frames are mainly for access purposes.

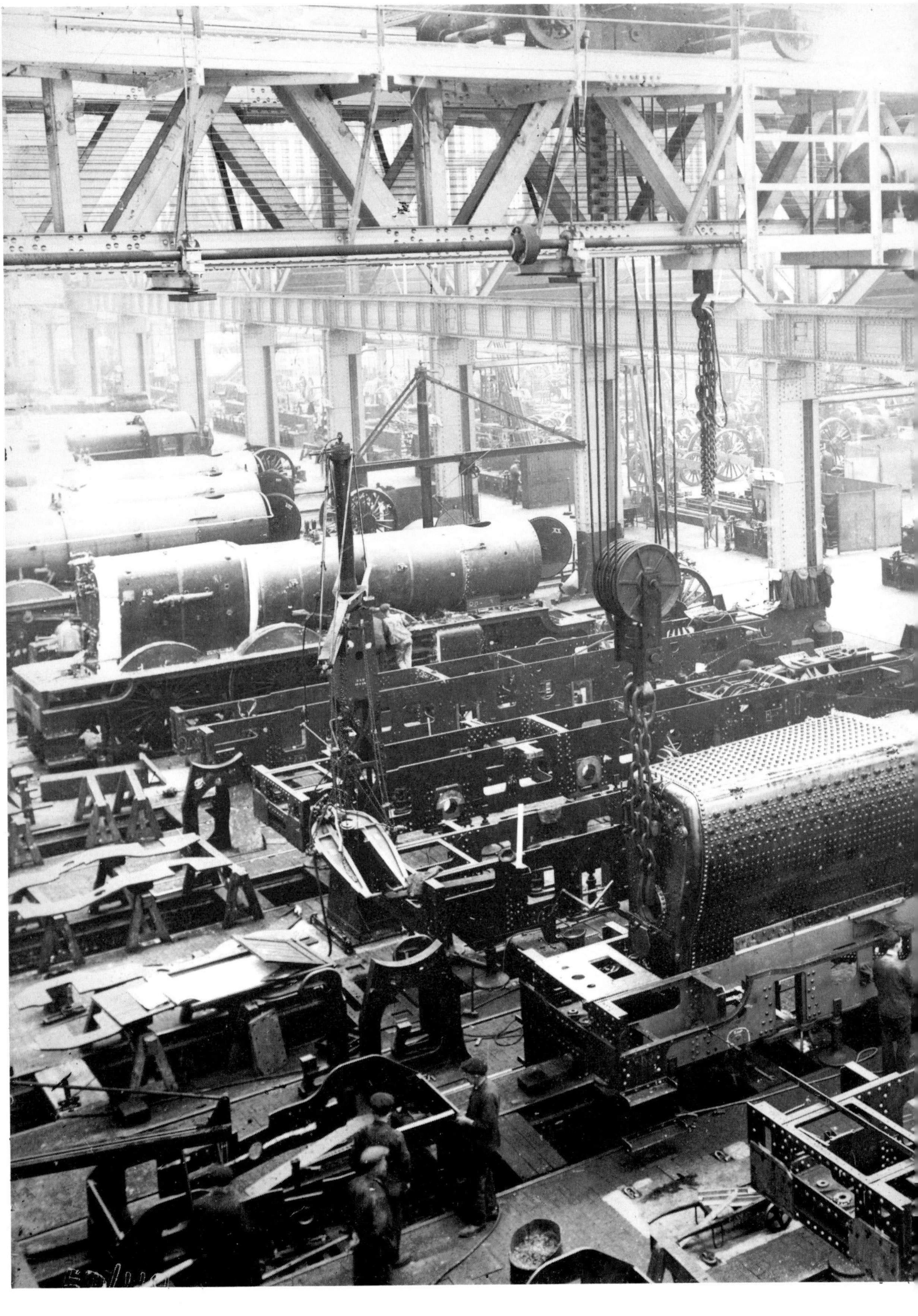

84 A general view of the five pits used for new erection with five locomotives in various stages of construction. Locomotives in the final stages of building are on the left, while the wheel shop is in the background. The boiler is being lowered onto No 2 frames — note the height of the travelling crane, of which there are two to each bay, each having a capacity of 100 tons. Also note the expansion brackets attached to the firebox and resting on the frames. Behind each locomotive are the frames for the bogies.

85   This view shows the axleboxes
fitted to the horns with the horn
stays fitted. They will then be taken
off and the boxes taken out, finish
bored and bedded on the
appropriate journal of the driving
wheels. The vertical structure on the
right carries a balanced jib to which
is attached a deep throated hydraulic
rivetter, and this machine is seen on
several of the following photographs.

86   Another view of the boiler
being lowered onto No 2 locomotive.
The outside and inside cylinders
have been fitted as well as part of
the motion, as it is far easier to fix
these before the boiler is put in
position.

87   The smokebox is being bolted
to the saddle casting. The four
pistons and piston rods (screwed in
and pegged) together with other
parts are ready in the foreground.

88

89

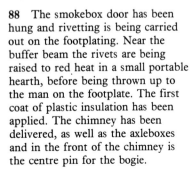

88 The smokebox door has been hung and rivetting is being carried out on the footplating. Near the buffer beam the rivets are being raised to red heat in a small portable hearth, before being thrown up to the man on the footplate. The first coat of plastic insulation has been applied. The chimney has been delivered, as well as the axleboxes and in the front of the chimney is the centre pin for the bogie.

89 On the wheels behind the locomotive the axleboxes are being bedded to the journals. In those days this entailed blueing the journal, lowering the axlebox onto the journal, lifting it off and scraping the bearing surface of the box. This operation was repeated until a satisfactory bearing surface was obtained. Each was then inspected and passed. Later with more accurate measuring and machining these operations were practically eliminated.

90 The inside and outside cylinders have been fitted to No 1 locomotive, as well as the valve gear casting and part of the motion. Note the pair of exhaust outlets of the inside cylinders, behind which are the two for the outside cylinders. When the smokebox is in position a breeches-type casting will connect the two pairs into a common blast pipe. The wheel shop is in the background.

91 The driving wheels are in their approximate positions, each pair manned by two men (one to each axlebox, but partly hidden behind the wheels and cranks) to guide the boxes into the horn cheeks. The inside valve spindles were connected to the outside spindles by means of rocking levers, just visible near the outside valve cover.

92 The chimney has now been centred with the blast pipe and bolted up. The cab sides have been fixed ready for the roof. Cabs were later built up complete on a jig and

were fitted as one assembly. The coupling and connecting rods have been fitted. This picture shows well the Belpaire firebox and tapered boiler.

93 The locomotive is now on a temporary bogie, ready for valve setting; the outside steam admission pipes have been fitted. For valve setting a labourer with a pinch bar was positioned at each coupled wheel and a fitter in the pit beneath marked out the quarters on one wheel and he controlled the men with the pinch bars in conjunction

with the valve setter positioned at the front end. The valve events were checked and any corrections were either effected by jumping (shortening) or hammering (lengthening) the eccentric rods by a blacksmith. Other adjustments could also be made to correlate the inside and outside valve positions. Valve setting was a specialised job and on the setter's skill depended the accuracy of the valve events and hence the efficient running of the engine, with a crisp, even exhaust beat.

92

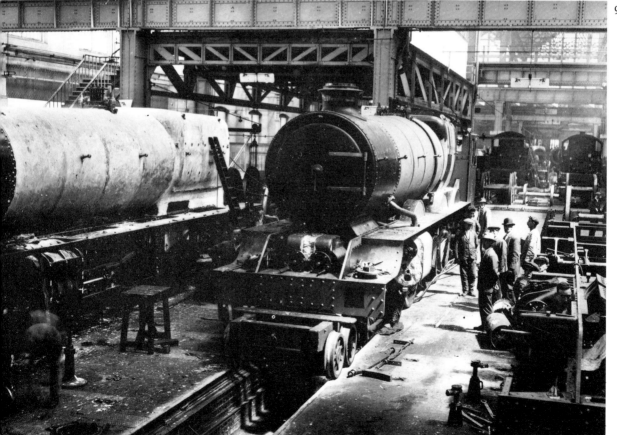

93

94 After valve setting the temporary bogie is replaced by the proper bogie: the locomotive being lifted at the front end and the bogie pin guided into its socket. This particular design of bogie was unusual in having leading wheels with outside bearings, but with inside bearings to the trailing pair of wheels, made necessary by the increased width of the inside cylinders. The outside steam pipes have been lagged and protected.

95 The finished locomotive in grey paint and lined out, posing for the photographer. After her trials she would be sent back for painting in the company's colours and varnishing. Usually new locomotives were painted in their final colours before trials unless photographs were required, such as the first of a new class. Even so, by this date many locomotives were photographed in their 'finished for the road' condition and not in the matt grey previously favoured.

95

Optical Alignment

To ensure free running and a minimum of wear to moving parts it was essential that the axles were at right angles to the cylinder bores and the distance of the axle centres relative to each other on both sides was correct. These factors were the prime influence in increasing mileage between visits to the repair shops. The established method of checking centres, frame squareness, etc, was as seen previously with simple equipment comprising trammels, straight edges, whipcord, callipers and the 'human touch'—sensitive or otherwise. A lot depended on the rigidity and levelness of the rails of the pits and an examination of photographs of various erecting shops show differences in the quality of the pits and the types of jacks and baulks used as supports. To achieve more accuracy in this field two important pieces of equipment were introduced: one was the Zeiss optical alignment equipment and the other was a pair of special-purpose grinding machines for grinding the horn faces.

96 This illustration shows the Zeiss equipment set up for checking the frame alignment of a 28XX 2-8-0 locomotive in 1934. At the front of the cylinder the operator is looking through the self-centering telescope sighting a graduated bracket and collimator which would indicate the accuracy or otherwise of the squareness of the horn blocks. From micrometer measurements taken across the horn-block faces, corrective treatment would be carried out. Note the well-laid bed of steel plating on which the frames are jacked up and levelled.

97 A close-up of the telescope with its self-centering spider. The rear cylinder cover is in place and this method obviates the need to remove it.

98 The collimator and axle centre tube are positioned between two horn blocks. From the centre-tube micrometer measurements will be taken to each horn cheek. (About 1930)

98

99 Another view of the telescope-and-collimator principle for lining up the cylinders with the frame, squaring the axles to the frame centre-line, spacing the axle boxes and setting the cross-head guides. This eliminated the heavy straight edges and squares, and only two men were required to carry out the survey. This is a German locomotive shown with its boiler in the frames.

100 The horn-cheek grinding machines showing the arm supporting the grinding wheel, in 1951. It was originally intended to traverse the arm through to the opposite pair of horn cheeks using one machine, but to increase production a second machine was installed to deal with the opposite side of the frames. Readings taken on the Zeiss equipment indicate how much metal has to be removed from each horn cheek. Anybody who has had to file and scrape work-hardened horn cheeks will appreciate the time and effort saved by this improvement. The frames are for BR class 4 locomotives.

British Railways class 4, 1951

101 In a number of locomotive workshops the frames for a locomotive or tender were built up complete with its stretchers, horns and ties. This method was later adopted at Swindon works and here a pair of frames for the BR class 4 4-6-0 have been completed. The frames were erected upside down for ease of assembly.

102 The frames have been delivered to the erecting shop. The pits have now been modernised with steel plates and no rails, and when ready for wheeling the locomotive will be moved up the shop to a railed pit. The cylinders, smokebox saddle and stretcher have been bolted in position as have the slide bars and motion brackets. The weigh-bar shaft is being lowered into position.

103 The piston, piston rods, crossheads and motion have now been fitted. Note that in the previous sequences these parts were left until the wheels, axles and cranks were in position. The cab sides have been put on for checking, but will be built on a jig.

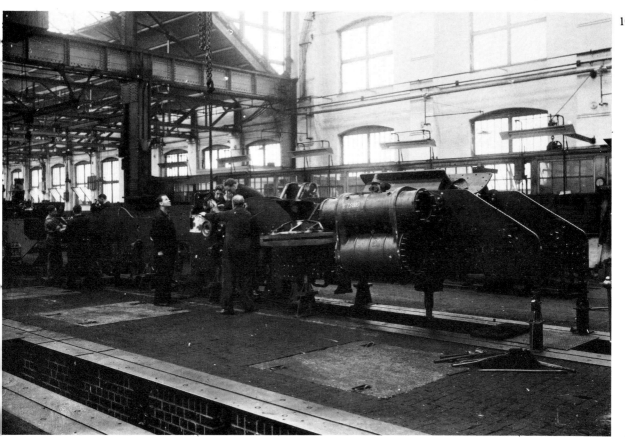

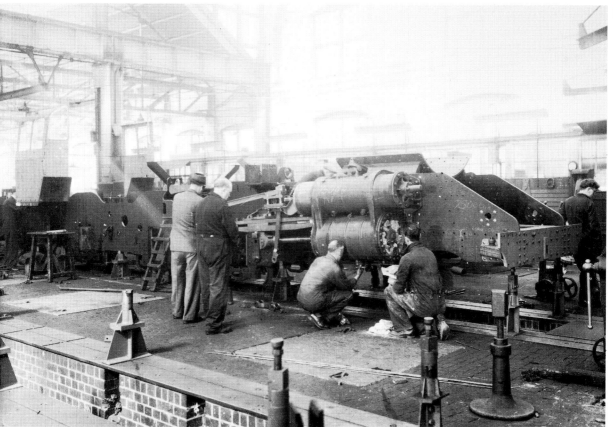

104 The coupling and connecting rods are being fitted. A fitter with a pinch bar is ready to move the wheel round to bring the crank pin into position. Note the automatic train control shoe at the rear.

105 A cab is being erected on a jig with a mixture of rivetting and welding techniques.

106 The boiler is being lagged with mattresses and rolls of insulation. Part of the cleading has been fitted to the rear of the firebox. All will be completed before the boiler is lowered onto the frames. Compare this insulation with the adjacent boiler which has the old type of plastic covering. Note the sight glasses for checking the water level in the boiler.

107 Another labour saving device was the introduction of the valve setting machine. The locomotive was supported on rollers whose centres could be adjusted to the class of locomotive for valve setting. The rollers were driven by an electric motor via reduction gears and were operated by the valve setter and his assistant by push button control. This eliminated the use of pinch bars for turning the wheels and speeded up the operation considerably with less man power.

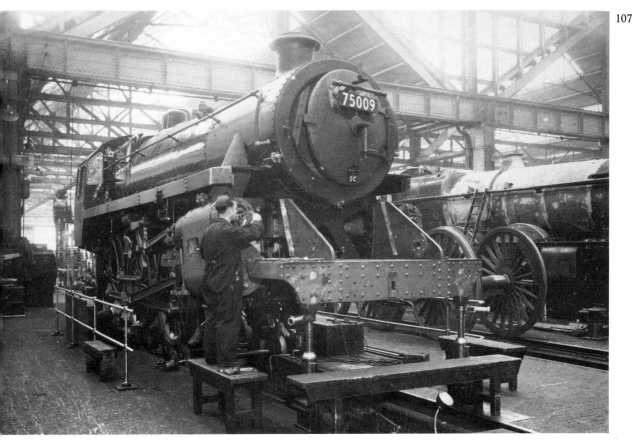

108 The completed 75001 in the hands of the painters. The painting of British Railways locomotives was not so costly or elaborate as on most railways before grouping, or even from the period of grouping (1921-2) to Nationalisation in 1948.

109 The tender frames for the BR class 4 4-6-0 being erected ready to receive the superstructure from the tank shop.

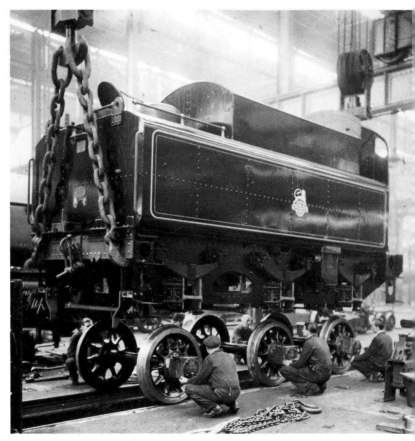

110 Wheeling the tender. The wheels were all fitted with Timken taper-roller bearing axleboxes. The springs are in position and everything has been painted.

Some Locomotive Erecting Shops

111 The GWR's West Yard, Cardiff, (ex Taff Railway) in 1926 just before closure. Note the absence of overhead cranes. The pits were served at each end by traversers. On the left is a K class 0-6-0 and next to it a class M1 0-6-2T GWR No 552, which was fitted for working the Pwllyrhebog incline. The Taff Vale Railway was the largest locomotive owner in Wales and eighty-four were built in their own works. Extensive rebuilding and repairs were also carried out here.

112

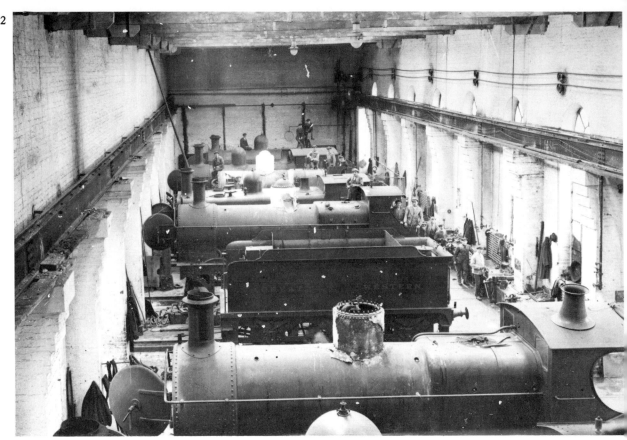

113

112 The GWR Oswestry erecting shop (ex Cambrian Railways) in 1926. This was also served by a traverser. In the foreground is an ex CR 0-6-0, while the next locomotive up the line is a 'Barnum' 2-4-0. The travelling crane was rope operated. This railway erected two new locomotives at Oswestry, but the boilers and frames were built by outside suppliers.

113 GWR (ex Rhondda and Swansea Bay Railway) repair shops at Danygraig, Swansea in 1926. Note the rope drive at high level along the right-hand wall for operating the overhead crane movements of traversing lifting and travelling. GWR outside-framed 0-6-0PT locomotive No 1582 is on the left; ex Powlesland and Mason 0-4-0ST GWR No 928 (built by Andrew Barclay Sons and Co Ltd) is on the centre road; on the right is ex R&SBR 0-6-2T No175 and another outside-framed GWR 0-6-0PT No 964 behind. No new locomotives were built at Danygraig.

114 The new erecting shop practically complete in the ex Rhymney Railway's works at Caerphilly in 1926. This type of erecting shop was modelled on Swindon AE shop with a central electric traverser feeding pits on either side and with travelling cranes high enough to lift one locomotive over another. No new locomotives were built here, but heavy overhauls and rebuilding continued until 1963 when the last locomotive left the works.

115   The North London Railway's Bow works erecting shop in 1891 with 4-4-0T No 47 after overhaul and 0-6-0Ts Nos 75 and 77 in process of being built with two further pairs of frames. For a small works the shop was very spacious, with plenty of operating room. The NLR built locomotives at Bow from 1863 to 1906 and during all this time only two types were built: 4-4-0Ts and 0-6-0Ts, the former were of two classes, the earlier with inside cylinders and then later with outside cylinders. The total output of the works was approximately 150 locomotives.

116   The North British Locomotive Company's Hyde Park works in 1927, previously owned by Neilson Reid and Co. One of the LMS 'Royal Scot' class 4-6-0s No 6142 is having its boiler placed in position. Note the angle iron around the boiler and firebox to which the cleading will be attached after the insulation has been applied. Behind can be seen No 6144 which already has had its cab fitted. The NBL Co was formed in 1903 with the amalgamation of three firms: Neilson Reid Co of Hyde Park Works, Dubs & Co of Queens Park Works, and Sharp Stewart & Co of Atlas Works making the company the largest locomotive builders in Europe at that time. The number of steam locomotives built from 1903 to 1958 was 11,318, and they were sent to all parts of the world.

117   LMS ex Midland Railway's Derby erecting shop with frames down for 2-6-4T No 2394 in 1933. Note that at this stage the erection takes place over a pair of rails without pit access. With outside valve gear the building up of the motion is made far more accessible. Note the temporary spacing bars between the frames. The first Derby works were the repair shops of the North Midland Railway which became part of the Midland Railway in 1844. The shops were enlarged from time to time and from 1851 to 1957 nearly 3,000 steam locomotives were built there.

118 Derby erecting shop in 1936
with more two-cylinder 2-6-4Ts
(batch Nos 2425-75) but differing
by being fitted with taper boilers.
Pony trucks and trailing trucks are
on the centre road, with the pit
exposed for the operation of
wheeling.

119 Derby paint shop in 1933 with
two 2-6-4Ts finished except for their
buffers. Very few locomotive works
had separate paint shops, but of
course the results were excellent,
aided by an even temperature and
the exclusion of dirt and dust.

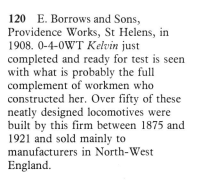

120 E. Borrows and Sons, Providence Works, St Helens, in 1908. 0-4-0WT *Kelvin* just completed and ready for test is seen with what is probably the full complement of workmen who constructed her. Over fifty of these neatly designed locomotives were built by this firm between 1875 and 1921 and sold mainly to manufacturers in North-West England.

121

122

121 Class A1 Pacific frames with cylinders, motion brackets and firebox support fitted at Doncaster Works, about 1923-5. A total of fifty-two locomotives of this classs were built. Other Pacifics were built later with many improvements to the valve gear, boiler, piston valves, draughting and other details. A streamlined version, class A4, built from 1935 to 1938 included *Mallard* No 4468 which on 3 July 1938 attained the world speed record for steam traction of 126mph, which has never been equalled.

122 An A4 Pacific No 4491 nearing completion in the Crimpsall erecting shops of the L&NER (ex Great Northern Railway) in 1937 at Doncaster. This was one of the few works which retained their separate paint shop. Bogie details may be seen in the foreground, with double coil springs to each axlebox. This type of bogie was used on earlier classes of Pacific, but No 4491's bogie had laminated springs. Doncaster works was completed in 1853 and from 1867 when the first was built until 1957, 2,223 steam locomotives were built. One of the

most famous locomotive designers H.N. Gresley, later Sir Nigel Gresley, was responsible for the design of GNR and LNER locomotives from 1911 to 1941.

123 Doncaster works in 1939. A 2-6-2 class V2 (batch 872-5) almost ready for wheeling and cab fitting.

124 Another V2 about to have the rods and motion fitted and coupled up at Doncaster in 1939.

125 LNER (ex Great Northern Railway) Crimpsall erecting shop at Doncaster. In the foreground is A1 Pacific 2574 *St Frusquin* after a general overhaul (originally built by the North British Locomotive Co in 1924). In front of it is a streamlined A4 Pacific. In the bottom left of the picture is a plan view of A4 cabs. New locomotives were built at the far end of the shop.

126 The LMS (ex London & North Western Railway) works at Crewe in 1939 with streamlined Pacifics Nos 6239 and 6238. The latter is ready for wheeling and is amply supported by no less than seven pairs of jacks and has its valance and streamlined cladding fitted, whereas 6239 has been wheeled first and not clad — note the supports for the streamlining around the boiler and firebox. This famous works was originally the shops of the Grand Junction Railway which moved from Edge Hill, Liverpool. The first locomotive was completed in 1845 and the last in 1958, the works having built a total of 7,331. Associated with Crewe were such famous locomotive engineers as Francis Trevithick, Alexander Allan, Ramsbottom, Webb, Bowen-Cooke, Beames, Hughes, Stanier and Ivatt.

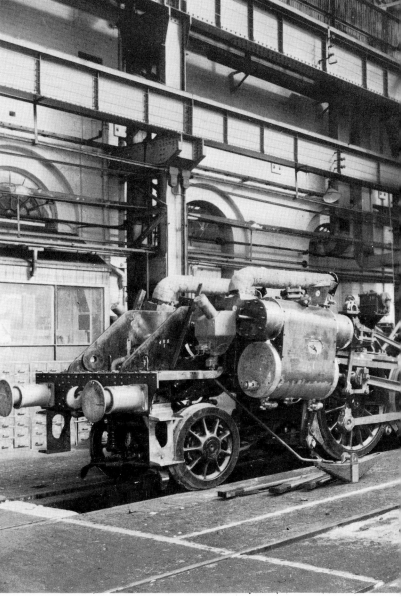

128 The Midland and Great Northern Joint Railway's works at Melton Constable, Norfolk in 1904. No 96, a 0-6-0T built here in 1899, is undergoing a general repair. Room appears to be at a premium with the number of locomotives under repair. Note the coupling and connecting rods with eccentric and straps. The round-topped boiler in the centre is for a new 4-4-2T being built. Nine 0-6-0Ts and three 4-4-2Ts were built during the period 1897 to 1910. The works were closed in 1930.

127 A British Railways class 9 2-10-0 No 92020 at Crewe in 1953 with wheels and motion (including reverser housing) all coupled up before the Franco-Crosti boiler was lowered onto the frames by the overhead crane. The large preheater can be seen fixed to the underside of the boiler.

129

130

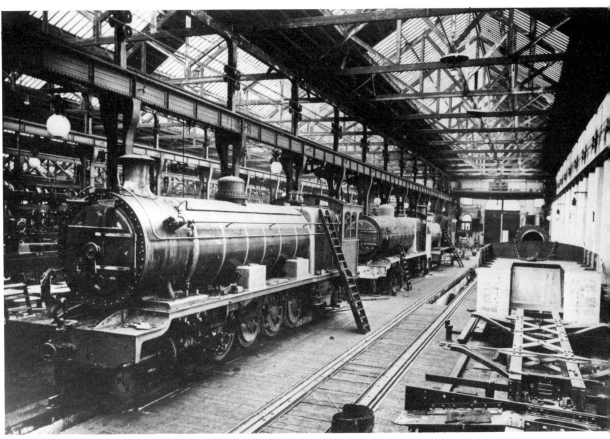

129 The Hunslet Engine Co, Leeds in 1902. The erecting shop had no railed pits. The locomotive in the foreground is one of two 0-6-0Ts supplied to the East London Harbour, South Africa, to 3ft 6in gauge and on the centre road is one of four 1-metre gauge 0-6-0Ts VA, No 21 for F.C. Vasco, Asturiana, Spain. This establishment together with its Kilmarnock associate Andrew Barclay Sons and Co Ltd is still building locomotives — diesel now of course. The Hunslet Engine Company was founded in 1864 and produced 2,236 locomotives of all types with a large proportion going abroad. To date the last steam locomotive built was completed in 1971 for the Indonesian Forestry Commission.

130 The North British Locomotive Company, Atlas Works, formerly owned by Sharp Stewart & Co Ltd, in 1912. A line of South African Railways class 12 4-8-2s 3ft 6in gauge, part of an order for eight locomotives (SAR Nos 1494-1501). The machine shop is in the background.

131 W.G. Bagnall Ltd, Castle Engine Works, Stafford in 1925. The two 0-6-0STs in the foreground are being built for stock. Excellent work was carried out in this erecting shop, but conditions were far from ideal with little space between the pits and pillars. Beyond the saddle tanks are some 4-8-0s being built for the Madras and Southern Mahratta Railway's 1-metre gauge. Established in 1875, the first locomotive, a 0-4-0ST, was completed in the following year, and many four and six coupled tank locomotives of the firm's own design were built and could be seen in many parts of the world. Main line types were also built and by 1957 1,667 steam locomotives had been built.

132 Bagnall's erecting shop in 1925. Two sets of frames have been laid down for 4-8-0s on order from the Madras and Southern Mahratta Railway. The first locomotive has been wheeled and jacked up to make it easier for the fitters. In the foreground are two bogie frames being erected upside down for convenience. An ash pan for a boiler is being man-handled.

133

134

33 Bagnall's erecting shop in 1931. One of six 1-metre gauge 4-6-0s for the Assam Railways and Trading Company (No 57) is practically complete. The locomotive on the right is a GWR 0-6-0PT (8725-49 series). A narrow-gauge track ran along the centre of the erecting shop and via a small turntable enabling materials to be brought in from the machine shop on the left and the fitting shop on the right.

134 Bagnall's erecting shop in 1933, with a metre gauge 4-6-0 locomotive being built for the Gaekwars Baroda State Railways, India. The first one is nearing completion, with the front covers to the cylinders to be bolted on. The service bogie is on the centre track. Note the multi-gauge rails on the left.

135 Bagnall's erecting shop in 1949. On the left one of three 1-metre gauge 4-6-0 locomotives for Mewar State Railway, India, while on the right frames for a BR (Western Region) 0-6-0PT (order 8400-49).

136 Andrew Barclay Sons and Company Ltd, Kilmarnock, in 1905. Two 4-6-0Ts being built for the Dunderland Iron Company Ltd, Norway (works Nos 1032-3). They were standard gauge with 18 x 26in outside cylinders and 4ft 9in diameter coupled wheels. They became Danish State Railway Nos 494 and 495 and ran for about 45 years. A standard gauge 0-4-0ST is being built at the rear. A lot of other engineering work is being carried out at the rear of the shop, including large flywheels and cylinders for stationary steam engines.

137 The erecting shop at Andrew
Barclay Sons and Company Ltd,
Kilmarnock, in 1907 and although
some internal walls have been
removed it is clearly the same shop
as in the previous photograph.
Machinery is also being built and
repaired, mainly for collieries. The
locomotive on the left is Jersey
Railway 3ft 6in gauge No 5 *La Moye*
a 2-4-0T. On the middle road is a
standard gauge 0-6-0T for the
Llanelly and Myndd Mawr Railway
to be named *George Waddell* (works
No 1111), and a standard 0-4-0ST
behind.

138 Andrew Barclay Sons and
Company Ltd, Kilmarnock. The
erecting shop twenty years later filled
with LMS class 4 standard 0-6-0s
and tenders, part of an order for
twenty-five locomotives (4357-81,
Works Nos 1901-25) in 1927. At the
top of the left-hand road is a 0-4-0ST.
The shape of the Belpaire firebox
is very clearly seen here.

Locomotive Testing and Dispatch

Locomotives could be tested either on a test bed or on the track with a dynamometer car, or sometimes both methods were used. As there was only one test bed in this country (at (at Swindon) until the completion of the Rugby testing station in 1948, railways other than the Great Western Railway used track testing and those who possessed a dynamometer car could accumulate a mass of statistics and data relevant to the locomotive under test.

The stationary test plant could be adjusted to accommodate six- and eight-wheeled coupled locmotives and the flanges of each pair of wheels dropped into grooves on rollers. Brake bands on the roller shafts absorbed the power produced by the rotating wheels, which reached a speed equivalent to 70mph with the locomotive remaining stationary. The value of this method of testing was that standard conditions could be produced, excluding variables such as wind and weather which were encountered on the track.

Nevertheless the test bed was never fully utilised until modernised in 1936 and the majority of testing routines were carried out on the track using the dynamometer car and due allowance was made for all variables encountered during the trials. Before and after the tests the coal in the tender was weighed and the amount of water measured, so that the consumption of both could be known. The weight of the train behind was recorded.

During the tests the observer on the footplate recorded the steam pressure, regulator opening and cut off at certain times and this information was transmitted to the dynamometer car. In the indicator shelter another observer took readings of the smokebox vacuum, ash pan pressure and indicator card which gave the indicated horse power by calculation.

Pyrometers fixed at various positions gave the temperature of the smokebox, superheater entry and exit steam chest, feed water etc, and these were recorded in the dynamometer car together with draw-bar pull, analysis of smokebox gases, speed and steam chest pressure. After the test the chemical analysis of the smokebox and ash pan ashes was carried out, and the amount of oil used checked. From all this information an accurate picture was obtained of the locomotive's performance, its strong points and weaknesses. Improved front end design, draughting and steaming could follow from modifications resulting from the data obtained. In the last decade of the steam locomotive another form of testing was 'controlled road testing' which took the form of steaming the locomotive at constant rates of evaporation, speeds, and loads.

139

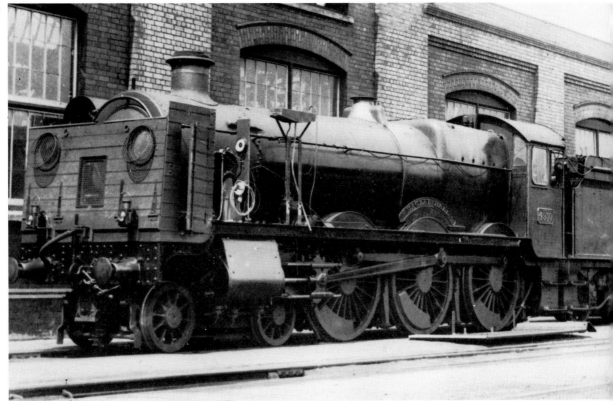

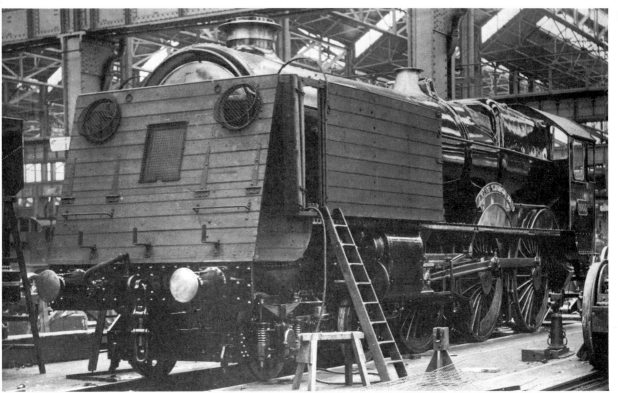

139 *Hall* class No 4930 in 1952 equipped with an indicator shelter attached to the dynamometer car, which will record the drawbar pull, speed, pressures, smokebox vacuum, various temperatures, indicator cards for each cylinder and many other readings. Coal, oil and water consumption and other important figures will all be assessed and modifications made to the class of locomotive if necessary.

140 *King* class No 6005 in 1931 being prepared for performance tests with the indicator shelter and instruments fitted. Some readings will have to be taken at the front end — hence the protection from the elements and to prevent the observer from falling off. This was a very hot and uncomfortable job, and an insulated suit would have been very welcome!

141 A test bed was designed and installed at Swindon in 1904 which could absorb 500hp and in 1936 it was modified so that it could absorb the maximum output of any type of locomotive suitable for this test bed. In the early days it was not often used, but later proved useful for fuel consumption tests, smokebox and draughting modifications and design. More information was obtained by road tests using the dynamometer car and this was used more frequently than the test bed. The latter proved a great attraction during the 1920s and 1930s when organised visits to the works became a weekly event. The locomotive on test is 6001 *King Edward VII* in the spring of 1953 running at an equivalent track speed of 75mph, prior to controlled

test runs between Reading and Stoke
Gifford (Bristol) with loads
approaching 800 tons (twenty-three
coaches).

142 Rugby testing station was
completed in 1948 and as it was
equipped with additional and more
sophisticated equipment it was used
to test many types of locomotives,
including all the standard BR classes
as they were built. These stationary
tests were combined in many cases
with tests on the line, including
controlled road testing with normal
and heavy loading and controlled
rates of combustion and evaporation.
On the test bed is one of the
remarkable BR class 9 2-10-0s No
92013. This class was quite capable
(though not encouraged) of working
express passenger trains at 70-
80mph, as well as the heavy freight
services for which were
designed. Note the multitude of
pipes by the cab side leading to the
instrument panels indicating
temperature, pressure, vacuum etc.

143 Class N1 0-6-2T No 4551 built in 1907, on the weighbridge at Doncaster works in 1933, after repair. This locomotive was fitted with condensing gear for working in the London area. Note the destination board brackets on the smokebox, vacuum brake pipe on the left of the coupling and the train heating pipe to the right. About fifty of this type were in the London area at one time for working suburban passenger trains, and goods traffic to yards on the south side of the Thames via Snow Hill.

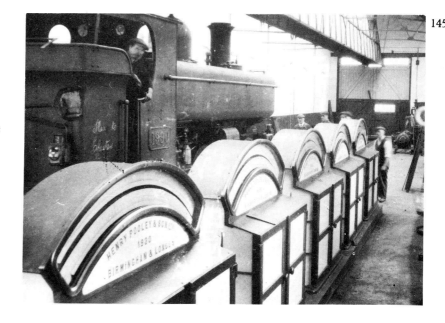

144 At Nasmyth Wilson and Company Ltd's Patricroft works, a 4-6-4T for the Federated Malay States Railway being prepared for a trial run with its safety valves blowing off in 1930. The Bridgewater Foundry was established in 1836 by James Nasmyth and many locomotives were built for home and aboard. The firm ceased production in 1939 by which time it had built 1,531 steam locomotives.

145 GWR, Stafford Road Works, Wolverhampton, in 1932. 0-6-0PT No 1990 (built at Wolverhampton in 1891) is on the weighbridge after an intermediate repair. There is a separate scale for each axle and the weight distribution can be adjusted by tightening or loosening the spring hanger nuts.

146 No 6028 having received a general overhaul and re-named *King George VI,* is brought out of AE shop at Swindon in January 1937 on the electric traverser to the apparent cheers of some of the workers. Note the experimental Jaeger speedometer drive fitted to the rear coupled-wheel crank pin.

147 The same locomotive being prepared for a trial trip to Chippenham later the same day. The tender has been coupled up, the fire lit and steam raised. The fitter is climbing up on to the footplate to check the steam pressure and the water level in the gauge glass. All other fittings would be checked and together with a driver and fireman the fitter and his mate or apprentice would travel on the footplate on the trial. If there was anything special in the way of fittings or modifications a locomotive inspector would join the others on the footplate.

148 The North British Locomotive Company Ltd, Glasgow, Queens Park Works (formerly Dubs and Co) in 1930. Eight 4-8-0s are ready for shipment and delivery to the Benguela Railway, in what is now Angola, Africa. They were part of an order for eighteen locomotives (Benguela Railway Nos 221-38). In the foreground are two spare boilers ready to go to an unknown customer.

149 A shipment of 4-6-0 locomotives and tenders awaiting loading on to a ship at Liverpool Docks in December 1924. These were built by the Vulcan Foundry Ltd, Newton-le-Willows for the East Indian Railway (works Nos 3741-80).

150

150 A specially posed group in front of the 3,000th locomotive built at Vulcan Foundry Ltd, Newton-le-Willows, in 1914. This was a 2-6-2T for the Great Indian Peninsula Railway (No 657), one of an order for twelve. This company commenced building in 1830 under the name of Charles Tayleur & Co. In 1847 the name was changed to The Vulcan Foundry Co and in 1898 became Vulcan Foundry Ltd. By 1933 India and Pakistan had been supplied with 2,800 locomotives and the Indian Continent remained their biggest outlet. The last steam locomotive built by Vulcan Foundry was tested on 13 January 1956 and altogether 6,210 were built.

Index